Contents

Numbers 1 - 5

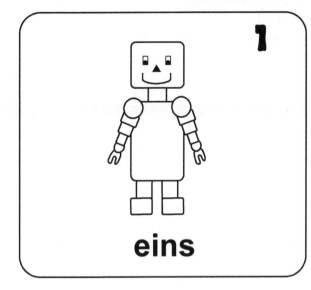

1

eins

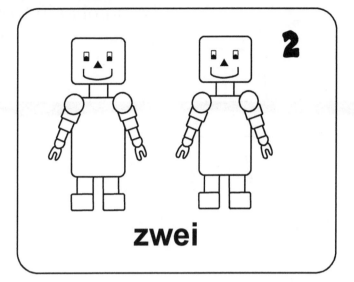

2

zwei

3

drei

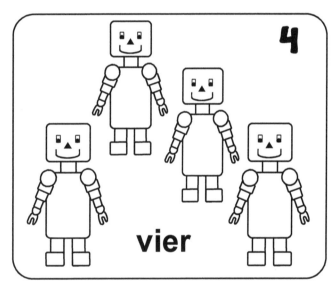

4

vier

5

fünf

Read the German numbers as you colour the pictures.

How many carrots are there?
(Write the number in German.)

a)

drei ✏

b)

_____

_____

c)

d)

_____

_____

e)

_____

Draw the correct number of apples:

a)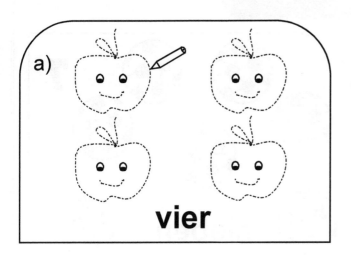

vier

b)

drei

c)

fünf

d)

zwei

e)

eins

 1 **2** **3** **4** **5**

eins zwei drei vier fünf

6

sechs

7

sieben

8

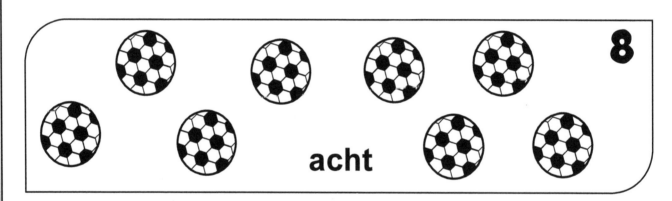

acht

9

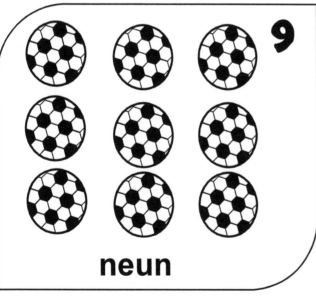

neun

10

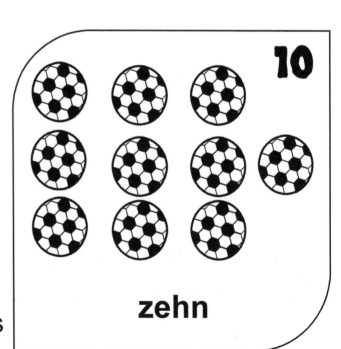

zehn

Read the German numbers as you colour the pictures.

How many bananas are there?
(Write the number in German.)

a)

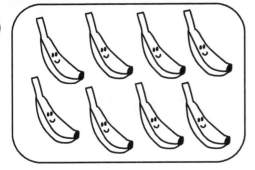

acht ✎

_____

b)

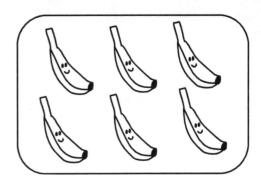

_____

c)

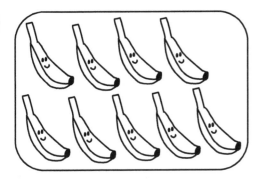

_____

d)

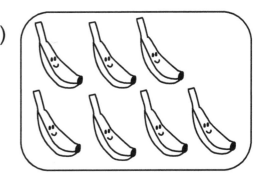

_____

e)

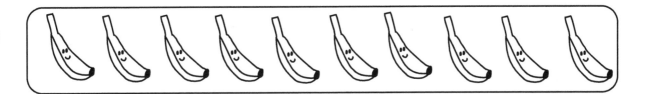

_____

6	7	8	9	10
sechs	sieben	acht	neun	zehn

5

Draw the correct number of strawberries:

a) **zehn**

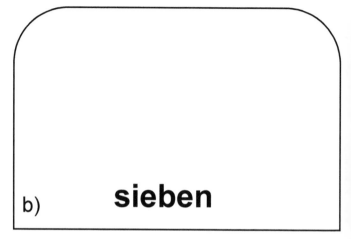

b) **sieben**

c) **neun**

d) **sechs**

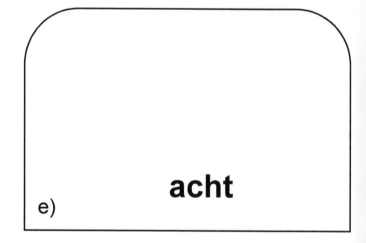

e) **acht**

6	7	8	9	10
sechs	sieben	acht	neun	zehn

Word search

E	I	N	S	A	H	K	I	L	U	H	G
K	Z	E	G	F	Y	F	J	Z	W	E	I
D	C	A	F	U	R	G	A	L	G	K	M
R	Q	H	Z	E	B	H	E	H	G	Z	O
E	Z	W	I	K	H	G	F	Ü	N	F	L
I	A	V	L	H	G	N	U	J	E	Z	K
E	I	Y	H	S	E	C	H	S	B	H	N
Y	A	Z	W	H	G	J	U	Z	H	E	S
V	C	U	N	E	U	N	V	F	B	F	Z
Z	H	D	R	H	G	Y	G	E	D	R	E
C	T	Z	W	H	U	J	I	G	Z	K	H
H	E	Z	E	G	Y	S	G	R	T	I	N

Find these words:

1	2	3	4	5
EINS	ZWEI	DREI	VIER	FÜNF

6	7	8	9	10
SECHS	SIEBEN	ACHT	NEUN	ZEHN

The teddy bear's picnic

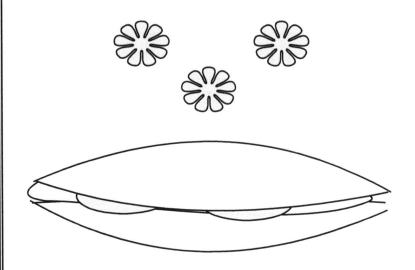

der Teddybär

das Sandwich

der Apfel

der Orangensaft

Colour the pictures as you read the German words.

Which German word is it?

Write the German words for the items pictured:

1) das Sandwich ✏

_____

2)

_____

3)

_____

4)

_____

der Teddybär   das Sandwich   der Orangensaft   der Apfel

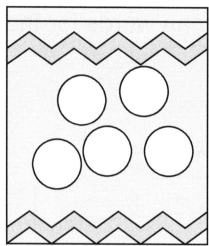

die Chips

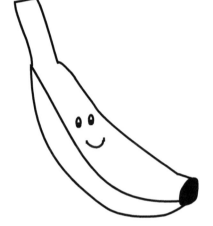

die Banane

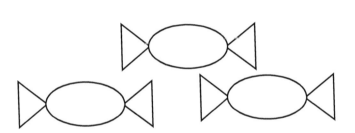

die Süßigkeiten

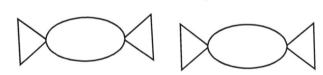

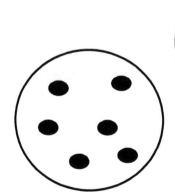

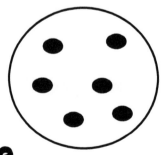

die Kekse

Which German word is it?

Draw a line from the object to the correct German word:

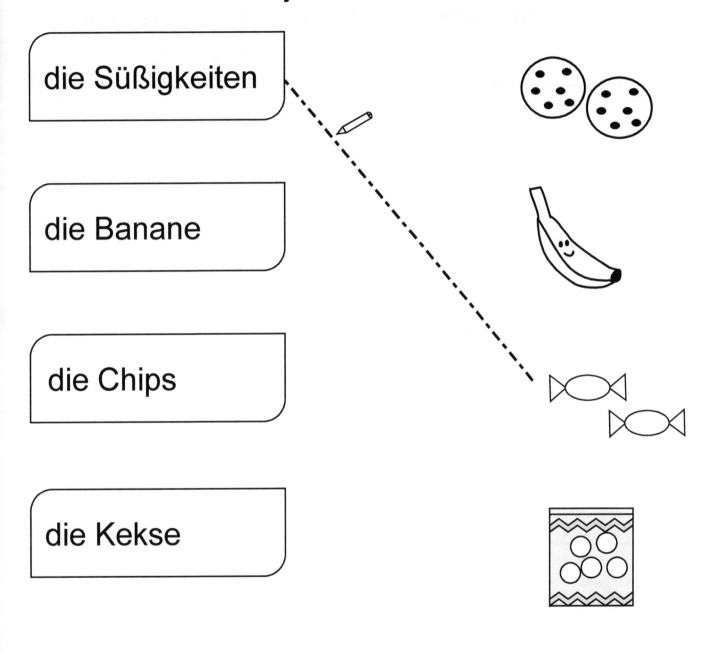

die Süßigkeiten

die Banane

die Chips

die Kekse

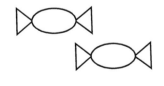

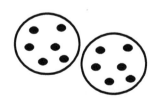

die Süßigkeiten   die Kekse   die Chips   die Banane

Circle the correct German word

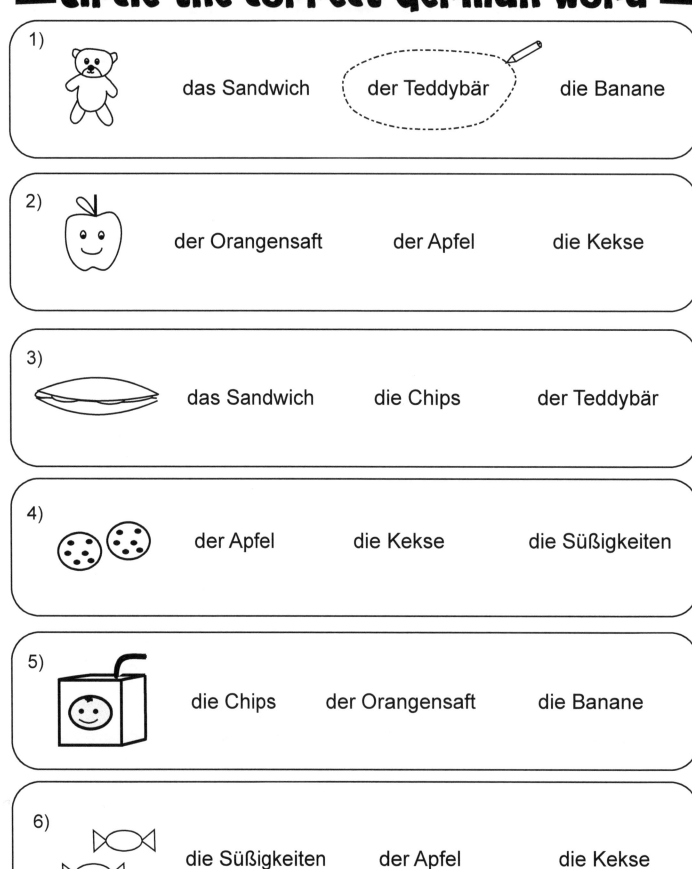

1) das Sandwich   (der Teddybär)   die Banane

2) der Orangensaft   der Apfel   die Kekse

3) das Sandwich   die Chips   der Teddybär

4) der Apfel   die Kekse   die Süßigkeiten

5) die Chips   der Orangensaft   die Banane

6) die Süßigkeiten   der Apfel   die Kekse

12

Word search

Find the following words:

SANDWICH   ORANGENSAFT   APFEL   TEDDYBÄR

O	R	A	N	G	E	N	S	A	F	T	A
Z	E	R	I	L	O	Ü	K	H	G	S	N
Q	R	L	E	S	X	F	G	Y	P	I	T
A	W	F	J	K	V	B	A	I	C	H	E
Q	P	S	A	N	Y	W	H	K	E	P	D
A	T	E	D	W	S	C	N	G	B	L	D
O	K	K	H	L	I	P	I	ß	Q	O	Y
R	E	T	S	A	N	D	W	I	C	H	B
A	K	S	O	V	Ä	C	A	Ü	P	L	Ä
W	S	T	B	A	N	A	N	E	J	K	R
C	E	K	V	S	U	I	L	Ä	W	H	Y
S	Ü	ß	I	G	K	E	I	T	E	N	P

    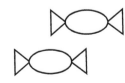

BANANE   KEKSE   CHIPS   SÜßIGKEITEN

13

Greetings

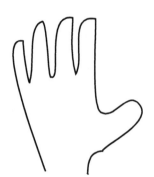

Hallo

(Hello)

Guten Tag

(Good day)

Guten Abend

(Good night)

Auf Wiedersehen

(Good bye)

14

Useful words

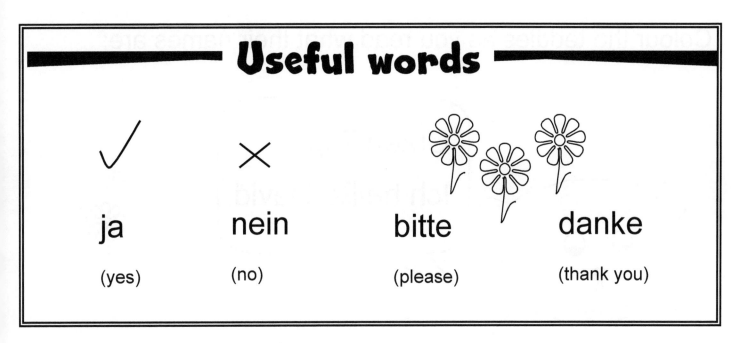

✓	✗	🌼🌼🌼	
ja	nein	bitte	danke
(yes)	(no)	(please)	(thank you)

1) Write in German how you would say the following:

a) yes   _____

b) no   _____

c) please   _____

d) thank you   _____

2) Write in English what the following German words mean:

a) nein   _____

b) danke   _____

c) ja   _____

Colour the teddies as you read what their names are:

Guten Tag!
Ich heiße David.

Guten Tag!
Ich heiße Emily.

Guten Tag = Good day   Ich heiße = My name is

Word search

G	U	T	E	N	T	A	G	H	Z	L	K	H	G
B	I	Y	G	F	G	U	T	E	N	G	A	O	U
D	A	U	G	O	H	J	N	G	F	R	C	Z	T
W	J	I	L	H	M	G	B	I	T	T	E	D	E
H	Y	L	J	G	D	A	N	T	Y	G	Q	D	N
F	A	I	K	H	U	E	V	C	S	N	Z	T	A
H	Q	M	N	B	K	V	J	U	G	E	Q	Z	B
I	K	U	H	N	G	B	G	F	V	I	Y	F	E
W	H	N	A	B	H	Y	G	A	T	N	M	K	N
R	T	D	J	K	H	J	A	U	K	H	L	U	D
F	J	L	K	I	H	Y	G	T	R	E	Q	P	J
A	U	F	W	I	E	D	E	R	S	E	H	E	N

Find the following words:

JA	HALLO
NEIN	GUTEN TAG
BITTE	GUTEN ABEND
DANKE	AUF WIEDERSEHEN

17

Colours

weiß

gelb

schwarz

grün

rot

blau

Colour the picture as follows:

rot - red   gelb - yellow   grün - green   blau - blue

(Schwarz (black) and weiß (white) has been done for you)

Farben (colours)

Colour the pictures using the correct colours:

rot - red   **gelb - yellow**   **grün**

rot

gelb

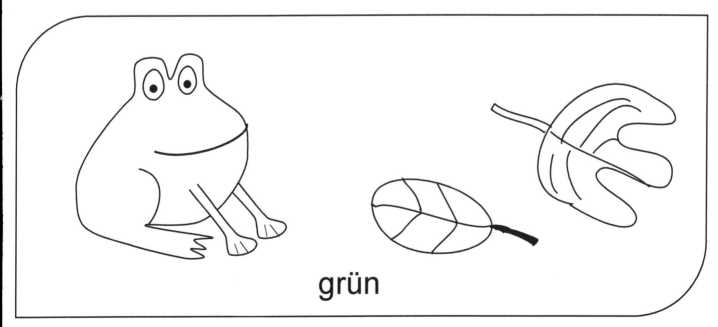

grün

19

What colour is it?

Write the colour in German for each of the things pictured:

1)

_____

2)

_____

3)

_____

4)

_____

5)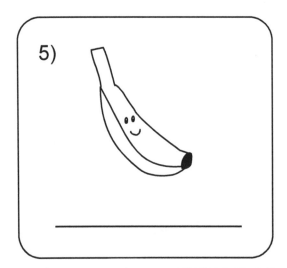

_____

6)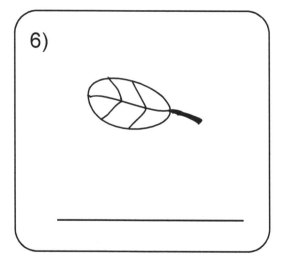

_____

rot - red   gelb - yellow   grün - green

German speaking countries

German is spoken in Germany, Austria and part of Switzerland.
Colour the flags for these countries correctly:

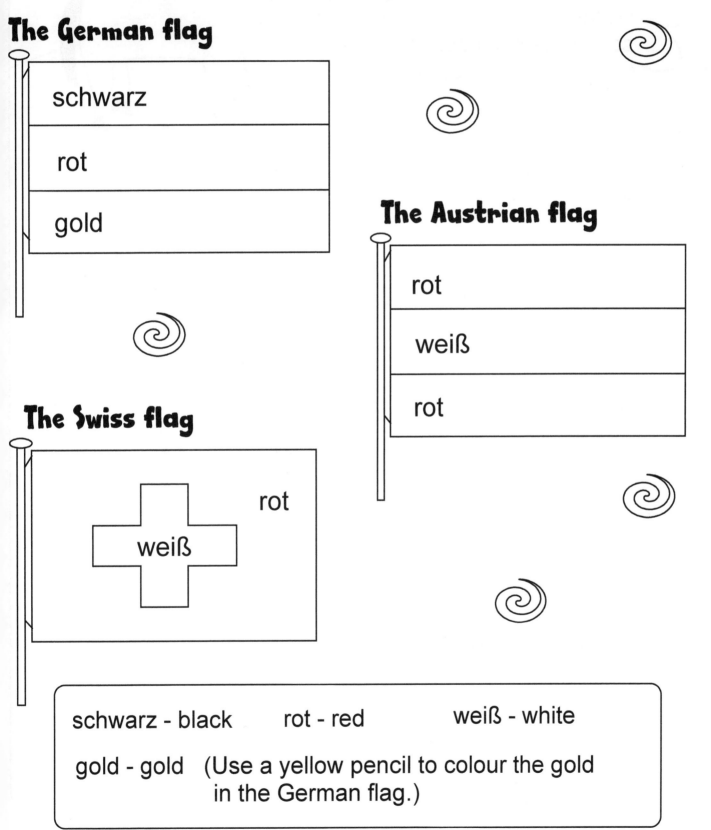

The German flag

schwarz

rot

gold

The Austrian flag

rot

weiß

rot

The Swiss flag

rot

weiß

schwarz - black   rot - red   weiß - white

gold - gold   (Use a yellow pencil to colour the gold
                    in the German flag.)

The farm

Read the German words as you colour the pictures.

das Pferd

das Schwein

das Schaf

die Kuh

das Huhn

22

Circle the correct German word

1)    das Schwein   das Huhn   die Kuh

2)    das Huhn   das Schwein   das Pferd

3)    das Schaf   das Pferd   die Kuh

4)    das Pferd   das Huhn   die Kuh

5)    die Kuh   das Schaf   das Pferd

das Schwein   das Huhn   das Schaf   das Pferd   die Kuh

Can you write the German words for the animals?

1)

2)

die Kuh

3)

4)

das Schwein   das Huhn   das Schaf   das Pferd   die Kuh

Favourite farm animals

Follow the lines from the children to their favourite farm animal. Then write the German word for the farm animal in the spaces provided under each child:

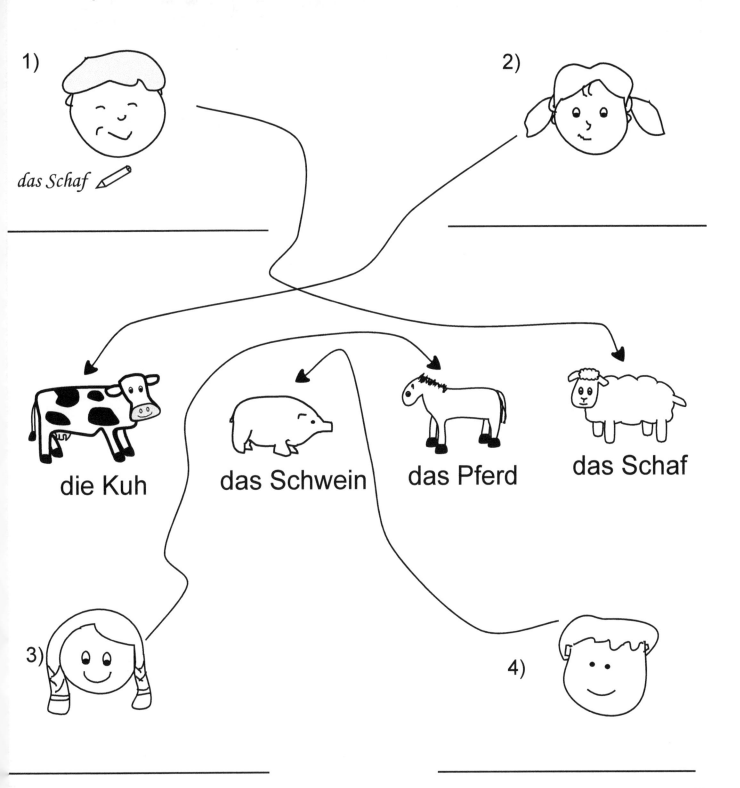

1)

das Schaf

_____

2)

_____

die Kuh   das Schwein   das Pferd   das Schaf

3)

4)

_____

_____

The garden

die Sonne

der Schmetterling

der Baum

der Vogel

die Blumen

Colour the pictures as you read the German words.

Copy the German words

die Sonne

die Sonne ✏

_____

der Baum

_____

der Vogel

_____

die Blumen

_____

der Schmetterling

_____

Circle the correct German word for each picture:

1)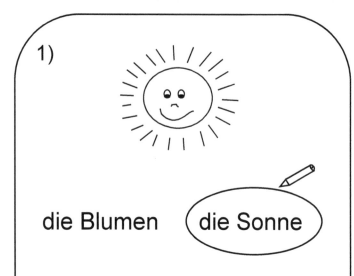

die Blumen   die Sonne

2)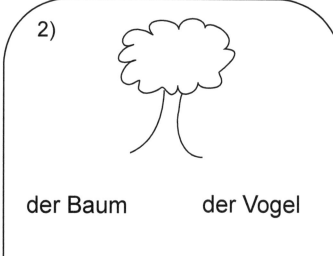

der Baum   der Vogel

3)

der Vogel   die Sonne

4)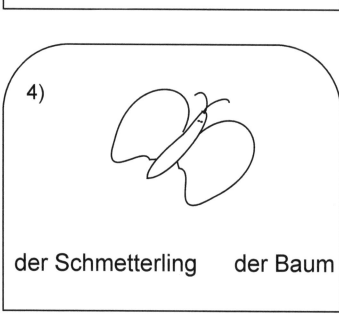

der Schmetterling   der Baum

5)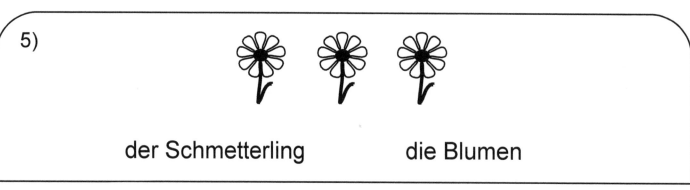

der Schmetterling   die Blumen

die Sonne   der Baum   der Vogel   der Schmetterling   die Blumen

Read the German words and draw the correct picture:

1)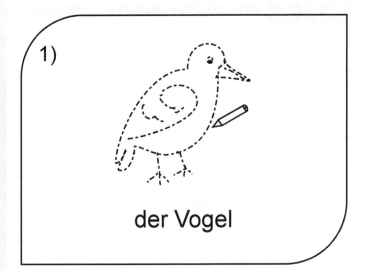
der Vogel

2)
die Sonne

3)
die Blumen

4)
der Baum

5)
der Schmetterling

die Sonne

der Baum

der Vogel

der Schmetterling

die Blumen

Vegetables

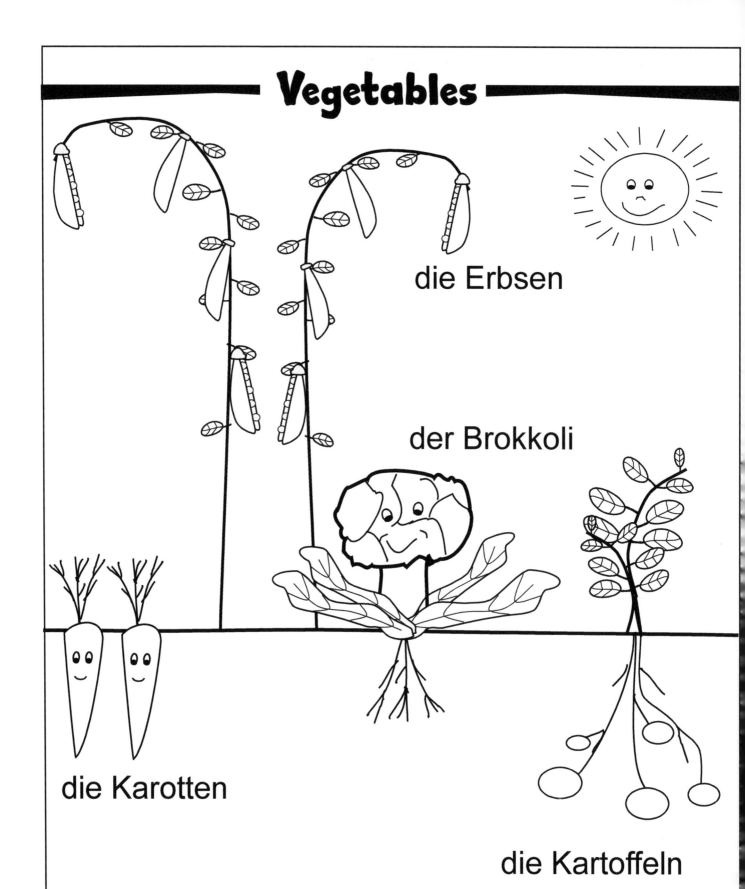

die Erbsen

der Brokkoli

die Karotten

die Kartoffeln

Colour the pictures as you read the German words.

What vegetables can grow in our gardens?

Copy the words and the pictures

 der Brokkoli

der Brokkoli ✏️

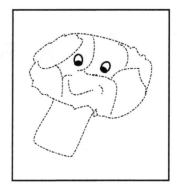

_____

 die Karotten

_____

 die Kartoffeln

_____

die Erbsen

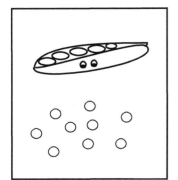

_____

Word search

```
K A R T O F F E L N E R B
C N V W Q A L K A R B O R
S E O K B L U M E N E R O
O Q G W G A O N P L C H K
N A E M S C H B A U M J K
N B L B E R B S E N K U O
E Z J K Y T R O T W Y S L
L K A R O T T E N Q Z P I
S C H M E T T E R L I N G
```

Find these words:

 KARTOFFELN

 BROKKOLI

 ERBSEN

 KAROTTEN

 BAUM

 SONNE

 VOGEL

 BLUMEN

 SCHMETTERLING

Toys

die Puppe

der Ball

der Teddybär

das Auto

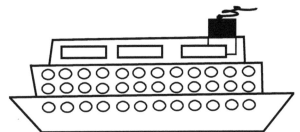

das Schiff

Colour the pictures as you read the German words.

What are the toys called in German?

Write the German word for each toy:

1)

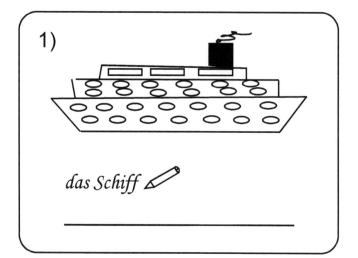

das Schiff ✏

_____

2)

_____

3)

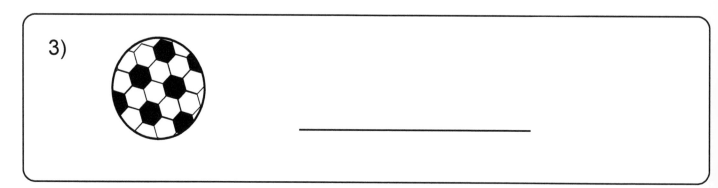

_____

4)

_____

5)

_____

 der Teddybär   der Ball   die Puppe   das Auto    das Schiff

Favourite toys

Follow the lines from each child to discover what their favourite toy is. Write the German word for the toy on the lines by each child:

1)

die Puppe ✏

_____

2)

_____

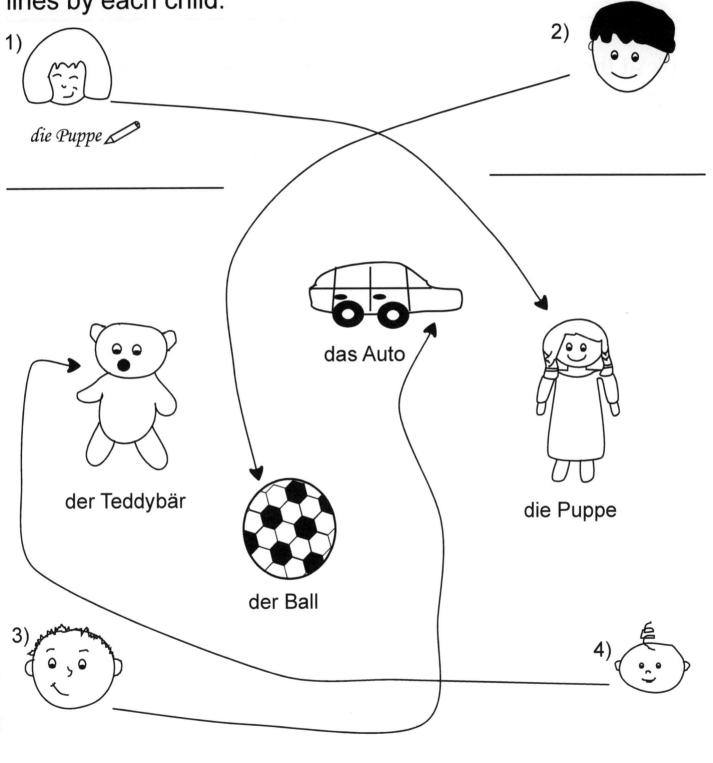

der Teddybär

das Auto

die Puppe

der Ball

3)

_____

4)

_____

der Teddybär der Ball die Puppe das Auto  das Schiff

Look at the pictures below, and draw a line to the correct German word:

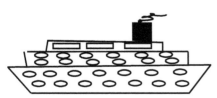

der Ball

der Teddybär

die Puppe

das Schiff

das Auto

Eine Kugel Eis, Bitte.

(A scoop of ice cream, please.)

Imagine you would like to ask for a scoop of ice cream in German. Copy the German words below, and draw your ice cream :

Eine   Kugel

_____ _____

Eis,   bitte.

_____, _____ .

Ice cream flavours

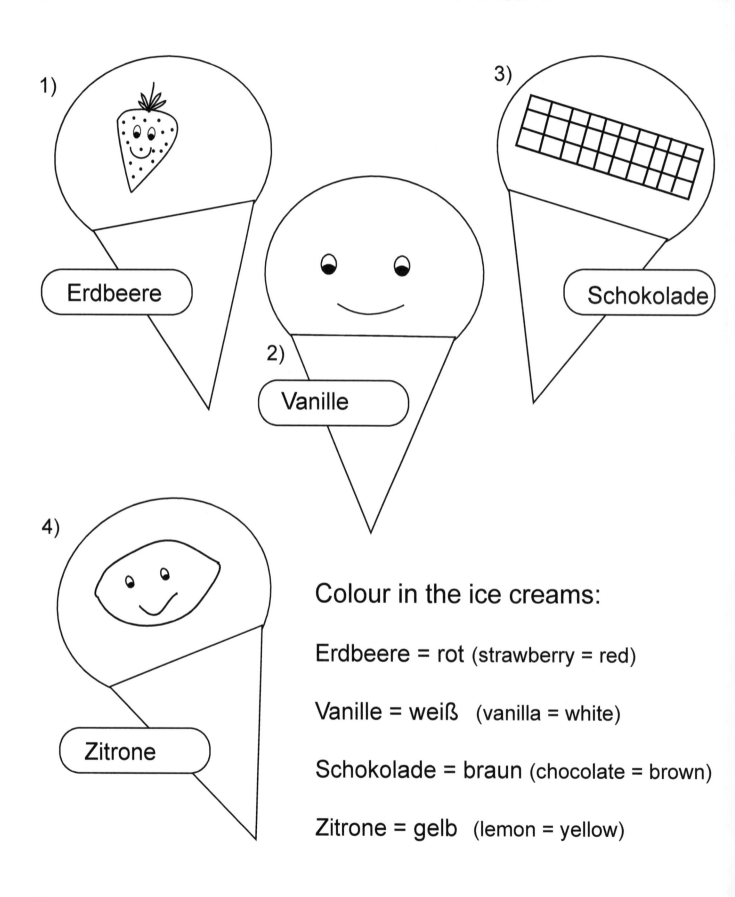

1) Erdbeere

2) Vanille

3) Schokolade

4) Zitrone

Colour in the ice creams:

Erdbeere = rot (strawberry = red)

Vanille = weiß (vanilla = white)

Schokolade = braun (chocolate = brown)

Zitrone = gelb (lemon = yellow)

Which ice cream flavour is it?

Circle the correct German word for each ice cream flavour:

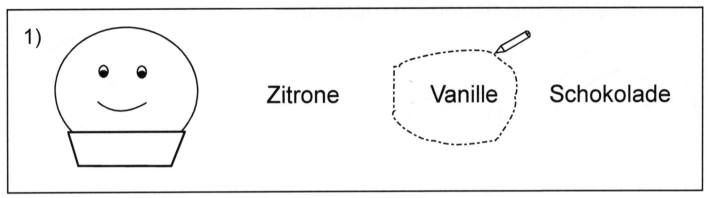

1) Zitrone   Vanille   Schokolade

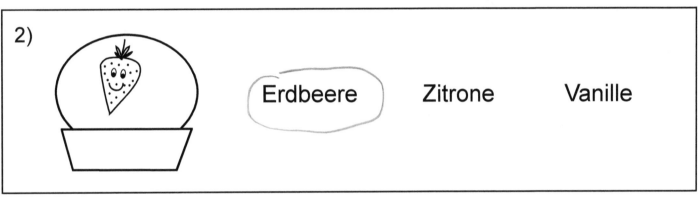

2) Erdbeere   Zitrone   Vanille

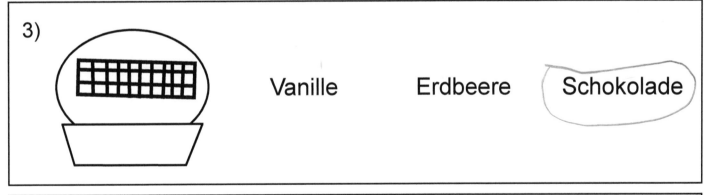

3) Vanille   Erdbeere   Schokolade

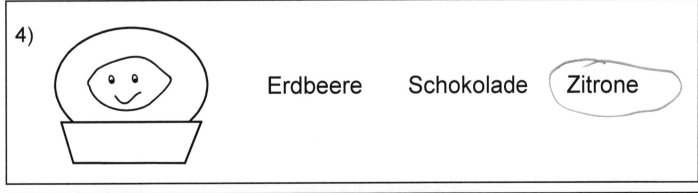

4) Erdbeere   Schokolade   Zitrone

Vanille - vanilla   Zitrone - lemon   Erdbeere - strawberry   Schokolade - chocolate

Favourite ice cream flavours

Follow the line from each child to their favourite ice cream flavour. Write the flavour in German.

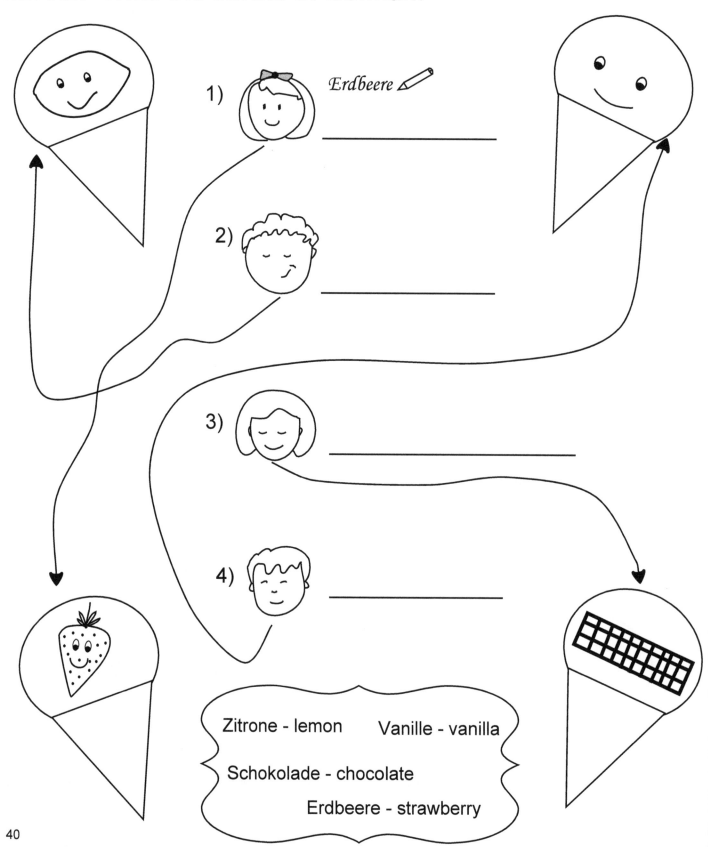

1) *Erdbeere* ✏

2) _____

3) _____

4) _____

Zitrone - lemon   Vanille - vanilla

Schokolade - chocolate

Erdbeere - strawberry

Answers

Page 2

a) drei   b) eins   c) zwei   d) vier   e) fünf

Page 3

The following number of apples should be drawn:
a) four   b) three   c) five   d) two   e) one

Page 5

a) acht   b) sechs   c) neun   d) sieben   e) zehn

Page 6

The number of strawberries should be:
a) ten   b) seven   c) nine   d) six   e) eight

Page 7

E	I	N	S						
						Z	W	E	I
D				R					
R			E						
E		I			F	Ü	N	F	
I		V							
		S	E	C	H	S			N
	A							E	
	C	N	E	U	N		B		Z
	H				E				E
	T			I					H
			S						N

Page 9

1) das Sandwich
2) der Teddybär
3) der Orangensaft
4) der Apfel

Page 10

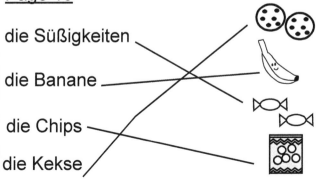

die Süßigkeiten

die Banane

die Chips

die Kekse

Page 12

1) der Teddybär
2) der Apfel
3) das Sandwich
4) die Kekse
5) der Orangensaft
6) die Süßigkeiten

Page 13

O	R	A	N	G	E	N	S	A	F	T	
				L					S		
			E				P		T		
	F					I			E		
P					H				D		
A				C					D		
K									Y		
E		S	A	N	D	W	I	C	H	B	
K										Ä	
S		B	A	N	A	N	E			R	
E											
S	Ü	ß	I	G	K	E	I	T	E	N	

Page 15

1a) ja   b) nein   c) bitte   d) danke

2a) no   b) thank you   c) yes

Page 17

G	U	T	E	N	T	A	G				G
											U
			O								T
		L				B	I	T	T	E	E
	L										N
A					E			N			A
H			K					E			B
		N						I			E
	A							N			N
D				J	A						D
A	U	F	W	I	E	D	E	R	S	E	H	E	N

Page 19

rot = red   gelb = yellow
grün = green

Page 20

1) rot   2) gelb   3) grün
4) rot   5) gelb   6) grün

41

Page 21
The flags should be coloured as follows:

The German flag
black
red
gold

The Austrian flag
red
white
red

The Swiss flag

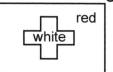

Page 23
1) die Kuh   2) das Schwein   3) das Schaf 4) das Huhn   5) das Pferd

Page 24
1) die Kuh   2) das Pferd   3) das Schwein   4) das Schaf

Page 25
1) das Schaf   2) die Kuh   3) das Pferd   4) das Schwein

Page 28
1) die Sonne   2) der Baum   3) der Vogel   4) der Schmetterling   5) die Blumen

Page 29
The following should be drawn:
1) the bird   2) the sun   3) the flowers   4) the tree   5) the butterfly

Page 32
```
K A R T O F F E L N       B
  V                       R
S O   B L U M E N         O
O G                       K
N E           B A U M     K
N L   E R B S E N         O
E J                       L
  K A R O T T E N         I
S C H M E T T E R L I N G
```

Page 34
1) das Schiff   2) der Teddybär   3) der Ball
4) die Puppe   5) das Auto

Page 35
1) die Puppe   2) der Ball   3) das Auto   4) der Teddybär

Page 36
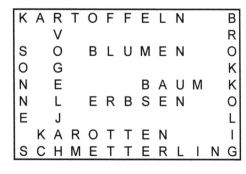

der Ball

der Teddybär

die Puppe

das Schiff

das Auto

Page 37
The ice creams should be coloured as follows:

1) red
2) white
3) brown
4) yellow

Page 39
1) Vanille
2) Erdbeere
3) Schokolade
4) Zitrone

Page 40
1) Erdbeere
2) Zitrone
3) Schokolade
4) Vanille

German	English
acht	eight
der Apfel	the apple
Auf Wiedersehen	Good bye
das Auto	the car
der Ball	the ball
die Banane	the banana
der Baum	the tree
bitte	please
blau	blue
die Blumen	the flowers
der Brokkoli	the broccoli
die Chips	the crisps
danke	thank you
drei	three
eins	one
Erdbeere	strawberry
die Erbsen	the peas
Farben	colours
fünf	five
der Garten	the garden
gelb	yellow
grün	green
Guten Abend	Good evening
Guten Tag	Good day
Hallo	Hello
Ich heiße	My name is
ja	yes

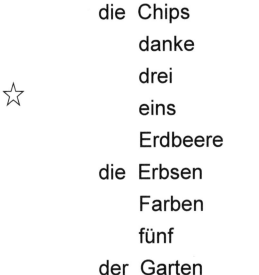

German	English
German	**English**
die Karotten	the carrots
die Kartoffeln	the potatoes
die Kekse	the biscuits
eine Kugel Eis	a scoop of ice cream
die Kuh	the cow
nein	no
neun	nine
der Orangensaft	the orange juice
das Pferd	the horse
die Puppe	the doll
rot	red
das Sandwich	the sandwich
das Schaf	the sheep
das Schiff	the ship
Schokolade	chocolate
der Schmetterling	the butterfly
das Schwein	the pig
schwarz	black
sechs	six
sieben	seven
die Süßigkeiten	the sweets
der Teddybär	the teddy bear
Vanille	vanilla
Zitrone	lemon
vier	four
weiß	white
zehn	ten
zwei	two

For children aged 5 - 7 there are the following books:

French
Young Cool Kids Learn French
Sophie And The French Magician
Daniel And The French Robot (books 1, 2 & 3)
Daniel And The French Robot Teacher's Resource book
Jack And The French Languasaurus (books 1, 2 & 3)

Spanish
Young Cool Kids Learn Spanish
Sophie And The Spanish Magician
Daniel And The Spanish Robot (books 1, 2 & 3)
Daniel And The Spanish Robot Teacher's Resource book
Jack And The Spanish Languasaurus (books 1, 2 & 3)

German
Young Cool Kids Learn German

For children aged 7 - 11 there are the following books:

Italian
Cool Kids Speak Italian (books 1, 2 & 3)
On Holiday In Italy Cool Kids Speak Italian
Photocopiable Games For Teaching Italian
Stories: Un Alieno Sulla Terra,   La Scimmia Che Cambia Colore,   Hai Un Animale Domestico?

French
Cool Kids Speak French (books 1 & 2)
Cool Kids Speak French - Special Christmas Edition
On Holiday In France Cool Kids Speak French
Photocopiable Games For Teaching French
Stories: Un Alien Sur La Terre,   Le Singe Qui Change De Couleur,   Tu As Un Animal?

Spanish
Cool Kids Speak Spanish (books 1, 2 & 3)
Cool Kids Speak Spanish - Special Christmas Edition
On Holiday In Spain Cool Kids Speak Spanish
Photocopiable Games For Teaching Spanish
Stories: Un Extraterrestre En La Tierra, El Mono Que Cambia De Color, Seis Mascotas Maravillosas

German
Cool Kids Speak German (books 1, 2 & 3)

English as a foreign language
Cool Kids Speak English (books 1 & 2)

For more information on the books available, and different ways of learning a foreign language go to https://**foreignlanguagesforchildren.com**

Lightning Source UK Ltd.
Milton Keynes UK
UKHW032221211220
375679UK00005B/186

9 781912 771806